NOTE: THE ABOVE IS AN *APPROPRIATION* OF A CIRCA 1789 INK DRAWING FROM THE MUSEUM OF FINE ARTS, BOSTON COLLECTION ENTITLED "THE END OF STRUGGLE" BY FRENCH ARTIST PETER *GOZINYA*. (OK, IT'S *NOT* REALLY FROM THE MFA COLLECTION!)

Stage Mother

ALLISON MET BRENDA HYDES IN COLLEGE THROUGH THE DRAMA CLUB. BRENDA WAS A BLUE-CHIP CHILD MOVIE STAR AND HAD MADE THE DECISION TO ATTEND AN IVY LEAGUE COLLEGE. BRENDA DECIDES THAT SHE IS JUST REGULAR FOLK AND DISAVOWS HER CAREER FOR THE SAKE OF BEING A COLLEGE GIRL. BRENDA'S MOTHER TRIXIE IS A CLASSIC STAGE MOTHER, AND GOES TO ALL THE REHEARSALS THAT THE DRAMA CLUB STAGES...

ALLISON DEAR, YOU REALLY KNOW HOW TO HANDLE YOURSELF WELL. I'M ORGANIZING A LITTLE PRESS JUNKET FOR BRENDA'S WORKOUT VIDEO "THE COLLEGE GIRL'S EXERCISE GUIDE," AND I'D LIKE YOU TO COME WITH US ON THE PROMOTIONAL TOUR AT THE END OF THE SEMESTER...

WHAT AN HONOR. I'D BE HAPPY TO...

WE'LL BE DOING RADIO AND TV SPOTS. YOU AND SOME OF THE OTHER GIRLS WILL DEMONSTRATE THE EXERCISES WITH BRENDA. WE'LL PAY YOU FOR YOUR TROUBLE.

3

SOME YEARS AGO, WHEN IN HIS LATE TWENTIES, *GEORGE* WORKED AS A SALESPERSON IN AN EXCLUSIVE HOLLYWOOD SHOP.

IN WALKS A FORMER MOVIE STAR, WHO NOW HOSTS HER OWN DAYTIME TALK SHOW. SHE LOOKS AROUND AND FINALLY SETTLES ON AN EXPENSIVE GOLD WATCH...

HOW WOULD YOU LIKE TO PAY?

I'D LIKE TO CHARGE IT TO MY SHOW.

OK. DOES YOUR SHOW HAVE AN ACCOUNT WITH US?

NO. BUT I'D LIKE TO CHARGE THIS TO MY SHOW.

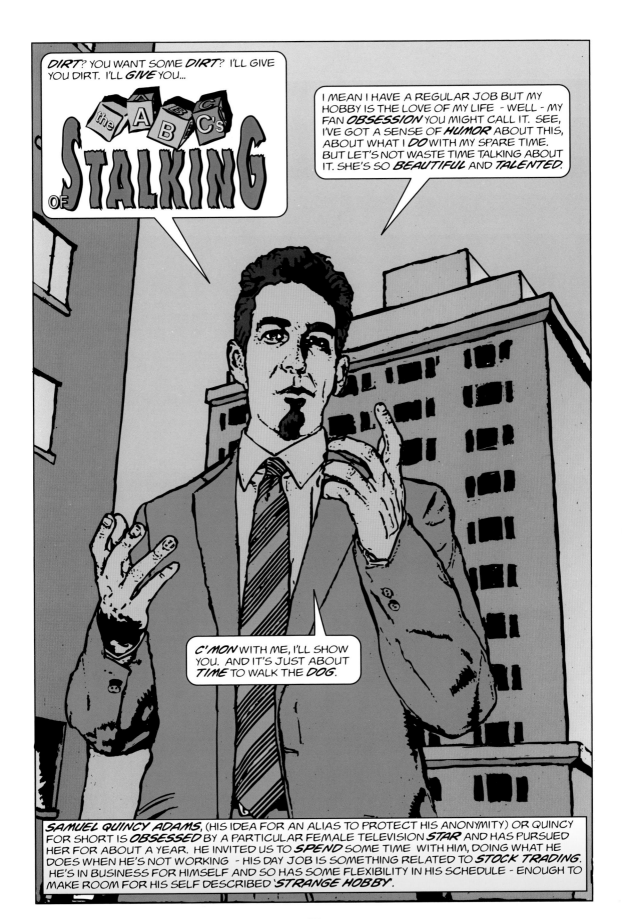

DIRT? YOU WANT SOME *DIRT*? I'LL GIVE YOU DIRT. I'LL *GIVE* YOU...

the ABC's of STALKING

I MEAN I HAVE A REGULAR JOB BUT MY HOBBY IS THE LOVE OF MY LIFE - WELL - MY FAN *OBSESSION* YOU MIGHT CALL IT. SEE, I'VE GOT A SENSE OF *HUMOR* ABOUT THIS, ABOUT WHAT I *DO* WITH MY SPARE TIME. BUT LET'S NOT WASTE TIME TALKING ABOUT IT. SHE'S SO *BEAUTIFUL* AND *TALENTED.*

C'*MON* WITH ME, I'LL SHOW YOU. AND IT'S JUST ABOUT *TIME* TO WALK THE *DOG.*

SAMUEL QUINCY ADAMS, (HIS IDEA FOR AN ALIAS TO PROTECT HIS ANONYMITY) OR QUINCY FOR SHORT IS *OBSESSED* BY A PARTICULAR FEMALE TELEVISION *STAR* AND HAS PURSUED HER FOR ABOUT A YEAR. HE INVITED US TO *SPEND* SOME TIME WITH HIM, DOING WHAT HE DOES WHEN HE'S NOT WORKING - HIS DAY JOB IS SOMETHING RELATED TO *STOCK TRADING.* HE'S IN BUSINESS FOR HIMSELF AND SO HAS SOME FLEXIBILITY IN HIS SCHEDULE - ENOUGH TO MAKE ROOM FOR HIS SELF DESCRIBED '*STRANGE HOBBY*'.

SO, I TRY NOT TO BE OUT HERE *TOO* OFTEN. I DON'T WANT TO *SPOOK* HER.

SHE'S GOT ENOUGH TO WORRY ABOUT WITH HER CAREER AND ALL WITHOUT HAVING TO FRET ABOUT SOME GUY *HASSLING* HER.

SHE THROWS OUT A LOT OF *GREAT* STUFF AND SO I COME HERE FOR HER TRASH ONCE OR TWICE A WEEK.

THE BUILDING'S A SECURITY BUILDING WITH A CLOSED CIRCUIT VIDEO INTERCOM, BUT THERE'S NO DOORMAN.

THERE IS A *SUPER* THAT KEEPS AN EYE OUT FOR HER THOUGH. THAT'S ANOTHER *REASON* THAT I KEEP MY DISTANCE IS THAT I DON'T WANT HER TO MOVE INTO SOME REALLY *SECURE* BUILDING WITH A DOORMAN AND ALL THAT. THAT SUPER IS A REAL PAIN. REALLY A BUSY BODY.

BETTER HIM THAN SOME *DOORMAN*, I MEAN THE SUPER IS GOOD 'CAUSE HE'S STUPID.

IF SHE *MOVED* THEN I'D HAVE TO DEAL WITH A DOORMAN. THEN I'D NEVER GET INTO HER APARTMENT AGAIN.

YEAH, I'VE BEEN *IN* HER APARTMENT...

SO, I PLANNED FOR A *MONTH*...

I BOUGHT THE UNIFORM AT A *UNIFORM* SUPPLIER'S AND WAITED UNTIL I KNEW SHE'D BE *OUT* OF THE CITY...

I MADE LIKE THE BOX WAS *REALLY* HEAVY...

I HAD *PLANNED* TO ASK TO USE THE JOHN, BUT THEN THE SUPER GOT CALLED *AWAY* FOR A MINUTE...

I HAD TO ACT *FAST*...

BINGO.

MOST OF THE **STUFF** I GET, INFORMATION AND PERSONAL ITEMS, I **KEEP**. SOME OF THE STUFF I USE IN THE NEWSLETTER THAT I RUN. I HAVE NEARLY A **HUNDRED** SUBSCRIBERS THAT EACH PAY **$25** FOR AN ANNUAL SUBSCRIPTION. I PUBLISH IT QUARTERLY.

I KEEP PEOPLE UP-TO-DATE ON **HER** COMINGS AND GOINGS, WHOSE COMPANY SHE KEEPS AND EPISODE INFORMATION ON THE TV SHOW.

I ALSO INCLUDE A **FEW** PHOTOS AND I **SELL** A FEW THINGS, PERSONAL ITEMS THAT I GET FROM HER.

I HAVE A GREAT **TELEPHOTO** LENS ON MY CAMERA AND I'VE TAKEN A LOT OF GREAT **SHOTS** OF HER.

AH, WELL I GOT TO GET TO THE **OFFICE**. SEE YOU **SUNDAY**?

A ZUCCHINI

AMERICA SUAREZ (NOT HER REAL NAME) IS THE COOK AT THE BOSTON TOWN HOUSE OF A LOCAL SPORTS STAR. THOUGH SHE LIKES HER JOB, AND ENJOYS THE PRESTIGE IT BRINGS HER, SHE CAN'T HELP BUT FEEL A LITTLE UNCOMFORTABLE WITH A SERIES OF INCIDENTS WHICH, THOUGH APPARENTLY INSIGNIFICANT, HAVE OFFERED HER A GLIMPSE INTO A PUZZLING AND ENTIRELY SECRET PART OF HER EMPLOYER'S LIFE...

I WAS IN THE KITCHEN ONE AFTERNOON.

HELL, I'VE LEFT A BAG OF GROCERIES IN THE CAR!

SO I WENT BACK OUT TO GET IT...

I DIDN'T KNOW WHAT TO DO. IT WAS ALL SO STRANGE. SO I WAITED. EVENTUALLY, I HEARD HIM COME DOWNSTAIRS...

AND DO YOU KNOW WHAT?! HE RINSED THE ZUCCHINI UNDER THE TAP, AND PUT IT BACK WHERE HE FOUND IT.

AS SOON AS HE'D LEFT THE KITCHEN, I RUSHED INSIDE...

SIR?

...AND CALLED UPSTAIRS. BUT THERE WAS NO ANSWER.

SO I JUST BUSIED MYSELF WITH THE DINNER, AS USUAL.

THAT ZUCCHINI JUST DIDN'T LOOK LIKE ONE OF THE BUNCH ANY MORE, THOUGH I CAN'T SAY WHY. WASN'T HALF AS COLD, NEITHER. I JUST COULDN'T MAKE IT OUT. MAYBE IT WAS ME. THERE MUST HAVE BEEN SOME REASON FOR THAT FUNNY BUSINESS. IT SURE WAS FUNNY, WHATEVER.

END

IT'S AN *ORDINARY* AND JUVENILE PRACTICE TO *DOODLE* ON THE FACES THAT WE FIND IN THE NEWSPAPER - EYE PATCHES, FANGS, NEW GAPS IN TEETH. IT'S RUDIMENTARY *ICONOCLASM* AND I AM AN ICONOCLAST AT HEART. MAYBE IT'S LEFT OVER ADOLESCENT REBELLION, MAYBE IT SIGNIFIES A *DEEPER* CONVICTION, BUT WHEN I SEE A PIE, I'M COMPELLED TO PUT MY *FINGER* IN IT.

AS NEW FORMS OR CELEBRITIES DEVELOP, THE EXISTING ONES ARE PUSHED ASIDE. LONG-TERM CULTURAL *SIGNIFICANCE* IS MORE A FUNCTION OF *PERSISTENCE* THAN INNATE *QUALITY* - SUPERSTARS ARE JUST SURVIVORS.

THE GAP BETWEEN *US* AND *THEM* IS ONE OF PERCEPTION. WHERE YOU ARE IS WHERE SOMEONE ELSE SEES YOU. ANOTHER VISUAL *METAPHOR* IS LIGHT DOES NOT EXIST WITHOUT SHADOW AND THE FAMOUS CANNOT BE THE FAMOUS WITHOUT THE ANONYMOUS. WE RISE AND SINK ACCORDING TO THE WHIMS OF INVISIBLE INFLUENCE.

THIS BEGS A SUNRISE/SUNSET MODEL. THERE PERSISTS THE *NAGGING* FEAR THAT WE'VE HAD OUR MOMENT - THAT WE'VE SEEN OUR BEST DAY AND DONE OUR BEST WORK.

IF THAT'S THE CASE - THEN WE ARE ALREADY *DEAD,* LIKE POOR JOHN KEATS WE'VE SLOWLY COUGHED UP OUR LUNGS. IF SO, AND THIS IS THE END...WE'D LIKE TO SAY THE WE *LOVE* YOU ALL AND WE *ALWAYS* HAVE.

OH, BY THE WAY - *LIES* ARE A PART OF SCANDAL AND TO DRIVE THIS POINT HOME, TWO OF THE STORIES IN THIS BOOK ARE COMPLETE *FABRICATIONS* AND TWO OF THE STORIES *REALLY* HAPPENED. MAKE YOUR BEST GUESS...

592-3668

WRITE US AT SPERANDIO@AOL.COM - WE'LL TRY REAL HARD TO WRITE BACK.